1/17 .

03. 01. 2022

# Suffolk Libraries

Please return/renew this item
by the last date shown.

**Suffolk Libraries**
**01473 263838**

**www.suffolklibraries.co.uk**

# The Chimney Swallows

by

Laurie Ogden

Illustrated by

Peter Newcombe

ISBN 1 85072 219 6

Printed in 14 on 18 point Palatino Typeface
by Sessions of York
The Ebor Press
York, England

*To the Children of The Pound*

*and*

*others who long for the swallows'*

*return*

William Sessions Limited
York, England

*'Why did all the Elms die, Grandad?'*

# The Chimney Swallows

Dear Kitty & Co,

I am lazing on an island in the sun and it is long past the time I should have begun.  Fortunately I remembered Horace once again and he has made me start your story.

If they still taught Classics at school you would know who Horace was and how he could make me start centuries after he was already dead.  I have started because Horace once wisely wrote  'He who has begun is half done.'

I am half done in the sun and must first move or I'll burn; but then I will begin.

'Oh do get on, Grandad!' as you grandchildren would say if you were all here.

It is a story for children but also for adults, if they will listen.  It begins in a time when if a boy and a girl fell in love they immediately thought they were very adult and would soon want to get married and create children.  And often and to their surprise then found that creating, caring and being responsible for those children made them less selfish, more the adults they had thought they already were.

So remember marriage creates adults as well as children. Which is why it is a good thing.

The Suffolk house these particular young married lovers came to was already very old.  It sat half hidden near the head of its own valley sheltered on two sides by high woods and behind by large trees.  The meadows between these banks of trees ran down to marshy ground, ponds and then a small river.

You felt it was built here because it was right.  Long ago before ever there were official planners to please or enclosures made, someone had come exploring up the main river from its estuary five miles away.  North of another inlet where Roman invaders of Britain had already decided to build their main city. The young explorers followed the river's first tiny tributary and then turned again into this yet smaller side valley, walking on up and finding at the head of its flowery meadows a clear spring of pure water that bubbled up through pebbles at the foot of a gravel bank. A bank that has nut bushes on it now.

Refreshed and sitting above that spring looking back down the valley he, or perhaps both, had simply said: 'This is where I shall build my house, our house.'

Centuries later there is still no other house nearer than half a mile away and the spring still bubbles on. I think it is as if everyone who has ever lived here has wanted most desperately of all to preserve for ever the charm of its solitariness and secrecy.

The central part of the present house – there would have been others since the Romans and before this one – was built around 1470. Between the beams of its timber frame, built on brick footings, there are walls of daub and wattle. That is a core of upright hazel rods each tied to its neighbour by leather thongs . . . so nut bushes already grew nearby even then . . . and these panels of wattle are then plastered over with a mix of clay, straw, horsehair and probably cow dung. They fill the spaces between the house's main timbers and long ago the old man, who owned this house before me, found weavers' tokens of

King Henry VII embedded in the daub of one wall. These are like coins and were used within the cloth weaving trade that flourished around here in medieval times.

There is still a deep hollow in the bottom meadow where the clay for the daub and for firing the bricks for the house was all dug out. A hollow now filled with bluebells and edged with bracken and great gnarled pollarded oaks. Just like those Arthur Rackham drew for other children's stories when I was a boy.

The centre of this oldest central part of the house is a massive brick chimney stack. This would have been the first part built. The original one built perhaps at a time when if you built a chimney stack on unoccupied common land and had smoke from your first fire rising out of that chimney by daybreak . . . you established your right to stay there.

But the chimney stack that was built here around 1470 would have taken more than one night to build. It had two big open fireplaces back to back on the ground floor and a third upstairs in the main bedroom. At its base the whole mainstack is 8 feet by 12 feet and its foundations go right down into and beneath a cellar. Each of its three fireplaces had a separate brick flue within that mainstack. You can stand in the biggest and look up at the sky. All three flues rise through the loft and roof to project as one big chimney for fifteen feet or so above the roof's main ridge. The bricks of the exposed part above the roof are laid in a projecting angled pattern so that the finished surface of the chimney's sides zigzag like the teeth of a huge saw. This and its age mean it is correctly described as a Tudor saw tooth chimney. This chimney belongs to my story. The house and the other buildings around it are what my story is built upon.

Now I will tell you one of its secrets. It is a house that has been written about before. Do you know Orlando, the marmalade cat? One of the stories about him is called *Orlando, His Silver Wedding*. And this house is the very same house which in that story Grace had to find to save Orlando from the Katnapper, one of two artists who lived here then. 'She went down a dark avenue of overhanging trees and found the pink house at the bottom'.

When that Orlando story was written the house was filled with animals as well as artists. Peacocks, macaws, cockatoos flying free, John Skeaping's horse in the orchard and, of course, cats and kittens.

Kathleen Hale, the author artist who created Orlando, changed some things about this house both in her story and her illustrations. Altering the house itself to look more like a cat!

'Like a cat, Grandad?' 'Yes, and she turned the Skeaping black marble torso in our brick courtyard into a stone cat madonna with kittens!'

'By magic?' asked Freddie apprehensively.

I too have altered some things in my story; time was and time when; made some things happen that didn't happen but that could have happened. Kept other secrets the house might not want told. Not many things, which is why it is not too tall a story.

The house is called 'The Pound' because it was originally the house of a special sort of farm. A farm that locally held the right to impound straying animals within its brick enclosures. Their real owners then had to pay a fee to recover their livestock. If any impounded strays were still unclaimed after a certain time the owner of The Pound could sell them to recover his keep costs.

Although those rights have long since fallen into disuse the name remains. Strangely, animals and birds still seem to stray back into its enclosures, stay a while in its quiet freedom and then disappear, back to where they belong.

Peacocks have come and gone; and strange bluey fawn long–tailed pheasant like birds with quills on top of their heads; muntjac and other deer peep out at the house from its surrounding woods; mallard flight in to nest on its ponds and each spring at least one pair of red–legged partridge leave the wide open fields to patrol the tops of its garden walls and find nest sites in its flower borders.

But by the time my story begins . . . 'Will the story EVER begin Grandad? We already know all about your house and its animals.'

'Yes, yes, but you live here, or at least you do sometimes. . . .'

'Anyway, as I was saying before you interrupted me Jessica . . .' By the time my story begins the artists and the parrots were all long gone. The house stood empty. The woods

*The lane's banks were all smothered with yellow aconites*

and undergrowth had crept across the fields nearer and nearer to the house, enveloping everything except the Catalpa lawn and south garden. The barn had burnt down. One studio, the one in an old granary, Lett's Studio, where the woodpile now is, had had its roof ridge broken by a falling ash tree branch, tilting the whole building dangerously across the lane.

And great elms that grew beside the farm's steep and sunken lane all met together over the top. Forming in summer a leafy dusky tunnel. You came down through this dark tunnel to find the secret house and the sun at the bottom. In the spring before the elm leaves came out the lane's banks were smothered with yellow aconites.

The old artist baronet who still owned the house had, although he loved it, to leave it. Because he loved it, he didn't want to sell. So instead leased it at a 'peppercorn' rent provided the new tenant never made any demand on him for any money for repairs. Old houses often do go through cycles of decay and resurrection as their owners get older and leave or die. Then someone new falls in love with the house and starts again.

Nine years after becoming his tenant I bought the house from him but I still had to agree an extra clause which said that

My Candle burns at both ends
It will not last the night
But oh my foes and oh my friends
It gives a lovely light

Bye bye Pound

April 1975

if ever Sir Cedric wanted, or needed in his old age to come back, he could build and live in a studio at The Pound. So you can tell he was like everyone else who has lived here. They often didn't want to go and never ever forgot the house. Another earlier tenant wrote with a diamond pencil on the glass of one of its windows:

'My candle burns at both ends
  it will not last the night
  But oh my foes and oh my friends
  it gives a lovely light . . .'

and then later just a faint 'Bye bye Pound' and a date.

'Did *you* have to have candles, Grandad?' said little Laurie, trying the switches to make sure the electricity was still there. 'Yes, we dined and went to bed by candlelight for nine years before the electricity reached this valley.'

But Sam was still only thinking about the big Elm trees and why they were no longer there. 'Why did all the Elms die, Grandad?' . . . 'Because some beetles wanted to live under their bark but carried in with them a fungus which the trees didn't like. The trees tried so hard to stop the fungus spreading that what they did also stopped their own sap rising. In the spring the rising sap feeds the new leaves as they sprout. So first their leaves died and without leaves the trees died. So they all had to be cut down.' 'Is that where all the wood on the woodpile came from Grandad?' 'Yes Lottie, and that too was when I replanted the lane with evergreen Ilex trees instead.' 'To have a dusky green tunnel to come down through all year round and to stop the snow blowing in and filling the deep lane until we can't get out.'

'Will you live long enough for the Ilex trees to make a tunnel again?' 'I don't expect so, Mat, but you may.'


As newcomers we arrived in March, nearly forty years ago after picnicking here in the south garden on a sunny February day when the snowdrops were out and when we fell in love with the empty ruined house.

To our surprise we found within a month of our arrival that The Pound filled with early summer visitors. They arrived in April. On the 21st precisely, although no letters had been sent to invite them.

They were the swallows. They all arrived together that year and with cries of joy began swooping in and out of doors and windows, skimming the pools and sweeping on down the valley to the river.

Soon the swallows were fetching mud and nest building. But to the newcomers' astonishment they chose to nest in only one place. Down inside their Tudor saw tooth chimney!

The brick divisions between its three internal flues had gradually since 1470 worn and been burnt so thin that parts fell down creating gaping holes high up between them.

The swallows would circle round and round the chimney stack and then unusually begin to hover directly above it, disappearing vertically downwards into the sooty caverns and crevices the broken flues had created.

'They always have' said the old artist who owned the house.

Two of the fireplaces had been closed up below and only the biggest still remained where huge log fires were burnt.

'Whoever lives in the house has to learn to light no more fires after the chimney swallows arrive. I should have told you.'

But the new tenants found all summer long they still had blue smoke coming out of their chimney. Blue swallows with touches of flame on their breasts endlessly rising up and down into and out of the top of the great Tudor chimney, building nests and later feeding their young.  They made a haze of blue smoke which broke up and drifted away down the valley.

The chimney swallows are the birds of my story.

As new tenants we had brought with us our first born, a daughter and her two young brothers.  Gradually the house got fuller and fuller.  This time with still more of our children, all girls.  And as all grew up parents and children learnt they only *shared* this house and valley.  Not just with the chimney swallows, but with owls, badgers and foxes;  with snipe in the marshy bits and woodcock in the snow.  One bitter cold dusk twenty-seven wrens were seen and counted squeezing through a hole in the weatherboarding of the Black Studio to huddle together in one protective feathery ball in the space behind. Safe from freezing until the sun came out again.

Blue tits nested in the house walls entering through tiny holes where oak pins had dropped out of ancient timbers.

Flycatchers nested above the garden door and in the summer cuckoos always came to the valley and one year some stranger birds, hoopoes.

The house also had some rather more difficult guests. There were bats and hornets in the roof. 'Oh I've never minded the hornets', said the old artist. 'They eat the wasps!' So the loft guests too were left undisturbed to share their part of the house.

The valley, its house, its wild guests and its other animals, horses, Jersey cows, beef calves, dogs, cats and bantams, were the centre of their lives. Once the children hurried back from the local town very upset and worried. They had seen a newspaper placard that said in very clear large letters: 'THE POUND LIABLE TO COLLAPSE'. There was only one Pound for them, but fortunately when they reached home that one was still there, just as it had always been.

The younger boy of this family was John Blaise and he is the beginning boy of my story.

It was when he was nine. It was his birthday and he had been given that morning a brand new bike, the first he had had with only two wheels. The Pound's lane was rough and steep so he had taken it to the next private lane. The one to the mill house on the river, just as rough and steep as ours where it reached the mill, but with a long level flat bit at the top before it begins to descend. There he practised nearly all that day until he could race it fast up and down this straight bit.

His father was hurrying home to join his son's birthday tea. 'Was that you, Grandad?' 'Yes, it was me and I was driving a little green van when this small boy on a bike shot out across in front of me.' Totally unexpected from that mill lane because the mill has a much better lane in from the bottom road and that was the one everyone always used.

Braking hard, there was barely a millisecond before the crash but within that moment I knew with crystal clarity that the small boy I was about to hit was my own son, John. Followed quickly by a moment of sheer relief as I struck and saw the boy fly clean over both his handlebars and my bonnet to land in tall grass on the other side of the lane.

But he had fallen against a little insignificant yellow concrete post, a marker for a fire hydrant buried there.

Silence and a crumpled boy in the grass who didn't rise.

*Silence and a crumpled boy in the grass who didn't rise*

His birthday was 20th February and before he came home again to be put to bed in a little room on the south side of the house it was April. So almost as soon as John was home and could see and talk but not walk the swallows arrived home too. That year they came on the 26th April.

John already knew that each year for several years now there were so many swallows that some of them had finally to overspill from the chimney and find new sites to nest in.

One year the outside doors at the bottom of the cellar steps, half way along the south side of the house, had been taken off to be mended.

Before the doors were replaced some swallows had started to build in the dark cellar below. Swooping down across the terrace directly at the house as if bound to crash into father's study window only to disappear at the very last second as they shot down the steps below his window and into the doorless dark cellar.

But that was not a good site to choose. Pushkin, The Pound's cat, not marmalade but a smooth haired tabby with four white socks, was a master hunter and soon learnt to sit on the terrace at the top of the steps and dab at them with his paws as they swept in or out.

John knew too that the swallows would even come into the house itself. Perhaps this started by accident because of their vertical chimney hovering being both unusual and difficult. Sometimes they couldn't make it back up or got it wrong in the dark, gave up and came zooming out of the fireplace into the room below. Even normally when hovering in the chimney they made a very characteristic noise. A noise that visitors couldn't understand and who were even more surprised when a swallow suddenly appeared in the room.

On the north side of that room there was one very old multi-paned window. Some of its panes still had smooth seventeenth century glass with bubbles in it and one single small central pane about 8 inches by 11 was the only part of the window that opened. So in the summer this tiny window pane was always left open so the swallows that came down the chimney could fly out again. Gradually even the inside of the house was becoming part of their territory.

They definitely liked to explore it. Because the valley was so sheltered and warm, doors and windows were more often open than not.  The swallows would sit on the edge of a likely entry twittering fast to each other about whether it would make a good safe new site or not, perhaps even a better way in to their chimney.

So John had an idea to solve the loneliness of lying on his back, bedridden, all day.  He pretended, despite the bats and the hornets, to hate having his bedroom window shut, whether it was sunny or wet, day or night.  Because he was so fragile and not  to be stressed, he got his way.

Soon a pair of young swallows, nestlings from the previous year, kept coming and sitting on the top of his open leaded light window, twittering hard, bending their heads down and peering in as swallows will.  They kept looking at John's big eyes and twittering harder still.  So he pulled his sheet over his face nearly to his eyes and lay very, very still.

After a time first one and then the other swallow each made separate quick circuits of his room and out again.  After several such sallies they began to come in and then hang for a moment in one particular darker corner which had a different ceiling angle to the rest and where a beam protruded an inch or two more than elsewhere.

*Sitting on top of his open leaded light window, twittering hard*

21

John said nothing and told nobody. The nest was half built before his mother knew. But she smiled and just put some newspaper directly beneath on the broad polished elm boards of the floor.

By the time his Granny came to stay the first brood had all hatched, the five babies always hungry and their droppings regularly piled up on the sheet of newspaper beneath. Granny was very houseproud and tidy. She didn't approve of swallows indoors and was used to getting her way in domestic matters. She muttered about fleas and lice getting into John's bed and creepy crawlies that the parent birds brought in being dropped down between the polished elm floorboards.

Sheets of newspaper appeared all the way from nest corner to window. That was after she finally had to agree the interest they brought was good for John and that she wasn't going to be allowed to knock the nest down with a broom!

Next she appeared with a large pepper pot. She had filled it with flea and lice dusting powder and she stood on a chair and shook it vigorously over the nestlings, under them and all around their nest. And then took pride in the fact that they seemed to grow faster and fatter than ever.

John now never minded how long he was left alone. His room was never dull. He had longed to see the first egg in the nest and count as others were laid, not just rely on his mother to tell him. When they had hatched he did count the number of feeding flights the parents made each hour and tried to identify and record what different things they brought. His father lent him his binoculars, but he still longed to sit up properly and even to walk again and get close. The parent birds were always a little apprehensive of John and any abrupt movement of his arms as they came in could make them turn and fly out again at once.

But the new nestlings themselves once they began to appear above the edge of the nest and look out had never known John not there. Often he was peering just as directly back at them and talking to them. They already knew all the movements he could make. They seemed to think he was just another rather big single nestling in his bed and couldn't understand why he didn't struggle to sit up to see more of the world as they were always trying to do.

There was one that he could identify. It always seemed the most active and it had slightly different feathering and colour pattern to its head. Not surprisingly when they were almost but not quite ready to leave the nest this one was the first to fall out.

John rang the bell for his mother and asked her to put it by him on his bed. And there, agitatedly at first but soon with more confidence, the parents resumed feeding it, even when two days later John transferred it to his shoulder. It was just as well Granny wasn't still visiting.

He called this one 'Sweep' in memory of its chimney ancestors and it was his favourite. He transferred it to his shoulder because, at last, some strength and control was returning to his back and he could struggle upright to sit against cushions.

His mother gave the swallows all the credit for getting this improvement.

After they left the nest the young birds didn't fly into the room very often, the outside world was too new and exciting. But he could still recognise Sweep occasionally and did so more often once his father had stretched a strong wire within his sight from the Catalpa tree to above his bedroom window. And as the summer ended it was there that his swallows would sit all in a row and talk to him. He thought it was about Africa and whether he would go with them.

When they were all gone, the window was closed. And because he was more lonely now his father often came to read to him. He liked *The Selfish Giant* best, because the birds did come back to that garden.

They talked a lot about swallows. His father told him that boys in Andalucia flew kites with hair snares attached to their kite strings to catch the birds high in the sky. That made him ask whether his swallows would have to fly over Andalucia to get to Africa for the winter and be at risk yet again as they came back?

One night John said 'Daddy, if our chimney swallows and their ancestors have always been coming to The Pound, have they always gone to the same house in Africa each winter? Do they nest again there, or only catch flies and eat? You said Mr. O'Brien was sending some of his stallions to Australia for our winter and expecting them to breed again during the summer downunder.'

Daddy didn't know. He thought if the swallows didn't nest again in Africa, it might not be a house they went to but just another lake or river estuary with plenty of flies and sun.

He did remember Mediterranean houses in the sun where swallows did nest, but the nests were built differently. Still of mud, but covered right over with a mud roof and with a side tunnel left to enter by. Perhaps they had been martins not swallows, or a different species. He promised to write to the Royal Society for the Protection of Birds for advice and more information.

John most often wished for two things. First that his bedroom swallows would survive and return in the spring and second that he could know exactly where they went every winter. They were so used to a house, his house, that he felt sure they must have a winter house far away in the sun as some of his parents' friends had.

Surely, if so, the two houses that had shared the same guests each year since swallows began ought to know each other. Could it be as magical a house as his? Did the swallows love it as much as they seemed to love his?

He imagined being well again and going to stay in that other house, how his swallows would twitter when they saw him in Africa. Perhaps there were children there too and if so, could they recognise each of his swallows as well as he could?

At Christmastime Granny came to stay again. She soon insisted on spring cleaning the nest in the bedroom corner. She would have liked to wash out its bedding but was not allowed to. She had heard John had had one of the swallows in bed with him so did all John's bedding instead. Putting Dettol in the water she used, so all the sheets smelt horribly for days.

But she had to be satisfied with carefully picking out all the swallows' loose feather bedding, dusting and shaking the pieces. Discarding the bits she disliked most and putting all the others neatly back again. She then added a few bits of her own to make it more colourful. More how she would like it if she had to sit in it for sixteen days!

And when John opened his Christmas stocking on his bed that year he found a tiny tin of flea and lice powder at the bottom. We know who told whom to put that in, don't we?

During his own holiday over that Christmas, John's father sat in his study and wrote a letter.

Royal Society for the Protection of Birds,
The Lodge,
Sandy, Bedfordshire.

<u>To whoever most appropriate</u>

Dear Sir,

I enclose a stamped addressed envelope because I would appreciate some specific advice and information about swallows.

Is there any detailed scientific monograph or good articles specifically on swallows?  If so, can you send me the appropriate references?

Some of the queries to which I need answers include: how precisely are the wintering locations of English nesting swallows known?  Have there been ringing trials with follow up information received?  Do they show the same territorial associations with domestic buildings in their winter quarters as here?  Do they have two breeding seasons, one here and one in Africa or wherever?

I have a small son who has been in bed since the spring following an accident.  He has been able to watch swallows nesting and rearing all summer. Their numbers here being so numerous and their attachment to this house so personal that some nested this year in his bedroom!

His interest aroused means I now need help to answer his continuous questions more accurately! Any at all would be appreciated.

Yours sincerely,


The New Year came and went. John Blaise in his bedroom had for a long time been counting the days off on his calendar. Not the number of days to Christmas or New Year or even to his own birthday, but the days to 16th April, which was the earliest his father had ever recorded the chimney swallows returning.

That year on 15th April, Alice, who helped with the horses in exchange for keeping her own here, came to tell him she had seen two nearby on Thorington Street reservoir on her daily ride. Two days later, Sheila, another helper at The Pound, saw one near the bull boxes. But it was not until 19th April that John saw his first one through his bedroom window, and although it didn't come in he was almost sure it was Sweep. . . .

Since the swallows had gone last autumn he had been praying for their safe return and making promises. 'Give me this and I'll do . . .' One night his father had heard him and said you shouldn't pray just for rewards, even for others or offer bribes. You should pray for a clear eye and steady hand, for the understanding and the strength to make things happen or to achieve things, perhaps even beautiful things, that would help God or that even God would admire. So he prayed again for Sweep's wings to strengthen so he could fly safe and high over the kites in Andalucia; for Sweep's eye to be clear to see the stars, or whatever else, he navigated by. And he set himself exercise goals for his own recovery and prayed for strength to achieve them, one by one. He had already walked round his bed with his mother's help before Sweep came home.

Sweep had a mate, a proper chimney swallow John thought, not one of his bedroom swallows. Sweep wanted her to nest in the bedroom and kept flying in until she agreed. But after taking one good look at Granny's bedding she started to build her own new nest directly on top!

Years later when we had a fire in the bressumer beam of the big fireplace and we had to have ladders up inside to make it all safe, we then found the chimney swallows always built on top of their old nests. Perhaps they got full of soot each winter from the fires and probably the lowest always took all the winter fire heat and finally crumbled and fell down. The most we found in one corner were seven nests all built on top of one another, all still holding firm.

John was steadily getting better but still spent a lot of time in his bedroom that summer. The bedroom swallows never minded *him* even though he was more active and would come quite close. But they were still apprehensive about anyone else coming into the room or near them.

Sitting or lying on the Catalpa lawn in the sun, John thought Sweep's mate sometimes returned to chimney hovering, whether for practice, nostalgia or to visit relations. One day he was sure he saw Sweep trying to copy her and follow her down. Certainly a few days later Sweep suddenly zoomed out of the fireplace into the old dining room, a room he'd never seen before. He flew round and round not finding, or not seeing, the tiny pane open for his more experienced relations' accurate exits. Instead he flew on into the hall and beyond to where John's father was and who stood up in surprise. This sending Sweep in a mad dash for the bigger window panes of that room's garden door. Only to crash into them at full speed and fall temporarily dazed to the floor. So his father picked up and put Sweep on his shoulder where he sat panting but quiet, perhaps remembering in his dazed way being fed on John's shoulder the previous year.

Afraid to call out and panic Sweep yet again, father just kept still and waited. Eventually John's mother looked in and crept away again fetching Kit, John's brother, with a camera, who took a photo of them, Sweep and father sat together.

Then father quietly said fetch the bird rings the British Trust for Ornithology lady brought that are in John's bedroom waiting to be put on the nestlings before they fly. So Sweep, before he recovered and flew off out through the open garden door, had a little light aluminium ring with a code number put on his leg.

When the photo was printed father didn't like it. He said Sweep looked fine but he himself looked much too fat and bald. John wished they had thought to photograph him last year when Sweep was being fed on his shoulder, but then remembered how the adult birds wouldn't feed Sweep if anyone else came in the room.

Before the swallows left that autumn, rings had been put on three clutches of fully fledged nestlings; two lots from the second bedroom nest and one, reached up an extending ladder, of real chimney swallows. And before they all left John was walking nearly normally and recovering his old energy and adventurous vitality fast. He must have, because that year he caught a 13.5lb. pike in the Brett below the bottom meadow. The field, where the old clay pit was and the pollarded oaks, a field they called 'The Park'.

Soon after that John went away to boarding school. Curiously and although he knew Sweep came back at least three more times, never again did the swallow have a mate that nested in the bedroom. Eventually the old bedroom's double nest was taken down on some occasion when the whole room was being redecorated.

John and his mother always gave a silent prayer of thanks for the swallows each April. And his father was heard to say, with a wry smile of humour . . . 'I've always found if I can survive the winter till the chimney swallows come, I'll last till the end of the year. So far anyway'.

But one year the chimney swallows didn't come.

*John and his mother always gave a silent prayer of thanks for the swallows each April*

34

April passed and early May and the house and valley which always had had swallows round it by then, had none.

On 10th May a solitary pair, then three together, arrived to fly around the stables and bull boxes, where some of the overspill in other years had nested. But the Tudor saw tooth chimney, even the whole of the house, had none. No strange hovering noises to disturb new guests, no need to make sure the little hinged window pane was always open. An association we had known for more than thirty years, the house perhaps for ever, was broken.

John, who was far away from home, was written to and told. Local enquiries revealed other East Anglians had lost many or all of their swallows.

Even the few late arrivals at The Pound didn't rear many young successfully, had fewer broods and didn't seem to stay around its buildings and valley in the same attentive way they once had.

Other years passed with few if any swallows. Massive winter gales devastated East Anglian woods, including nine acres at The Pound. The Black Studio's chimney stack was blown over and crashed down through its roof, wrecking it completely.  The top of the Catalpa tree was snapped off and blown clean over both the house and walled gardens falling in the stable courtyard.  Trimmed, that old tree survived and regrew, but the loss of both the woods edging and sheltering the valley and other garden trees depressed John's father.  To make things worse, someone trespassed and gassed all the badgers in The Pound's sett.

John's father hated change and seemed to get much older in that year.  He and kind friends and others from a University Zoology Department began experimenting with restocking the sett with TB tested badgers from elsewhere, but that is another story.  But he couldn't face the gale damaged woods and garden and began to let them all go wild encroaching back upon both his fields and house.

Then one midsummer a letter came to him from the British Trust for Ornithology who coordinate all the bird ringing studies, saying that one of their regular correspondents from Africa had been travelling in famine devastated Sahel and had noticed amongst the trinkets on a string round a young native woman's neck a British Museum bird ring.  He had taken its code number and got an interpreter to ask the woman about it.

Her husband had taken it from a dead swallow's leg in their valley some years before and given it to her to add to her lucky charms. The girl and her husband hadn't known what it was.

The British Trust for Ornithology thought John's father would like to know. It was the only one of those ringed Pound swallows that was ever traced. It was Sweep's code number.

John was still away. What had meant to be just a year off travelling had been extended into several as he drifted, often rather aimlessly, on. He was too uncertain of himself, consequently indecisive and too easily attracted by other people's more positive, even bizarre, ideas rather than finding his own. His father worried about him and his long absence.

When John was told about Sweep he diverted his travels and went to the African valley where the ring had been found. What he saw horrified him as a lot of other poverty and starvation seen on his travels already had. It made him more thoughtful. He began to feel it was time to come back to The Pound and decide what life was really about and what values should have top priority in his life.

By chance soon after he arrived back there were celebrations going on in the local market town. This town was twinned with Ste. Marie Terese le Bas, a prosperous market town in a southern part of France and their respective civic dignitaries liked exchanging visits. The ones from France were being entertained to oysters and feasting by their English opposite numbers with pomp and at considerable expense. There were photos in the local press of both civic groups in their robes and chains of office. John thought again about that chain of trinkets around a half-starved African woman and went home to The Pound.

Sitting on the wall of the dipping pool in the Catalpa garden and looking up at the Tudor chimney, he suddenly knew what he would do. He went up to his old bedroom, opened the window wide and sat down to write a letter. East Anglia is one of the few areas with its own local daily paper, *The East Anglian Daily Times*.

To its Editor, he wrote:

The twinning of our local town with a similarly prosperous one in France is currently being celebrated and mutual benefits flow from these social and commercial exchanges.

But perhaps a deeper benefit would follow if our local prosperity was linked with a similar sized but far less successful area, even one struggling to survive.

In recent years some of this poverty and starvation in far away places has begun to affect East Anglia directly in a rather unusual way.

Many East Anglians have noticed with sorrow an abrupt decline in the number of swallows arriving here each spring to nest in and around our villages. Some houses where swallows have always nested have lost them altogether.

Initially this decline was blamed on Subsaharan drought, the extending Sahara desert being always considered a major migration hazard. But the causes are now thought more complex.

Poor feeding both here and at traditional migration resting sites can cause heavy losses particularly in seasons with bad weather. This has been linked with reduction or loss of livestock, particularly cattle, whether through changed agricultural practices as here in East Anglia or through drought and starvation in areas of Africa.

Loss of livestock reduces fly numbers, diminishing the local swallows' food supply and fitness. This leaves them too weak to complete their long traditional migration routes. It probably also reduces breeding success amongst those that do survive.

I believe each Suffolk village or group of villages has long been naturally twinned with the village or area which was their own swallows' prime winter destination, and with one or more of the regular migration resting and feeding sites used en route. Swallows do show very clear territorial preferences which they adhere to year after year. If this natural twinning was made official, those territorial preferences would keep the areas of twinned responsibility helpfully small and personal. Some houses might even be directly twinned.

Specific support for B.T.O., R.S.P.B. and Water Aid charities could be used to research the detailed ringing and identifications needed to make such twinning feasible. Efforts to aid and improve the water supplies, irrigation and livestock husbandry of such identified twinned areas might then lead to reciprocal benefit, increasing the numbers of swallows returning safely to our Suffolk barns and houses.

Perhaps children in Africa would learn to identify and report more regularly ring code numbers. Particularly if they knew how such information, on their local swallows, might bring material help to their village.

Surely adoption of this natural twinning already created over centuries by our swallows, by helping the poorer area attain an improved quality of life, could bring friendship, dignity and pleasure to both communities?

Yours,

John Blaise

Suffolk 1994


John received many private letters in support of his idea and some official ones expressing interest in sponsoring it.

But for John and his family best of all was the response in his father who had thought John's wandering and drifting might never end.  He had begun not to care about the damage of the gales.  Letting the scrub and tangles it had left in wood and garden spread and encroach on The Pound again. As he got older, too old he thought, to begin again to restore, replant and maintain it, he imagined the place would become like it was the year he first found it long ago. Completely wild, hidden and overgrown, with only the Catalpa garden clear and facing the sun. He living there like a hermit down his sunken lane and his ideas of building surpassing beauty, continuity and inheritance in his valley abandoned and uncertain. 'If ever the silver cord be loosed and the golden bowl be broken' . . . 'or the son of man know not from whence he came. . . .'

But now John was repaying his old debt to the swallows; was home with fresh ideas worth living for and he himself, John's father, might live to see The Pound's chimney swallows back in another April . . . perhaps not long for the snowdrops were already out again under the nut bushes.

He knew too that he must restore his valley's old flowery hay meadows, bring back the cattle and clear its ponds. Helping to create plenty of flies and insects so any returning swallows could feed well and breed easily, rearing strong young better able to survive their tough annual migrations.

*For the snowdrops were already out again under the nut bushes*

Oh Kitty, you have fallen fast asleep!  I shall have to tell it to you again, or perhaps, as this time I *have* written it down, you and any other Children of The Pound can read it for yourselves when you are older.

L.O.
Madeira  November 14 – 28 1994
Quinta Penha da Franca and
Penha da Franca Mar.